Looking at an Angle

ENCYCLOPÆDIA BRITANNICA EDUCATIONAL CORPORATION

Mathematics in Context is a comprehensive curriculum for the middle grades. It was developed in collaboration with the Wisconsin Center for Education Research, School of Education, University of Wisconsin–Madison and the Freudenthal Institute at the University of Utrecht, The Netherlands, with the support of National Science Foundation Grant No. 9054928.

National Science Foundation

Opinions expressed are those of the authors
and not necessarily those of the Foundation

ISBN 0-7826-1544-9
1 2 3 4 5 WK 02 01 00 99 98

The *Mathematics in Context* Development Team

Mathematics in Context is a comprehensive curriculum for the middle grades. The National Science Foundation funded the National Center for Research in Mathematical Sciences Education at the University of Wisconsin–Madison to develop and field-test the materials from 1991 through 1996. The Freudenthal Institute at the University of Utrecht in The Netherlands, as a subcontractor, collaborated with the University of Wisconsin–Madison on the development of the curriculum.

The initial version of *Looking at an Angle* was developed by Els Feijs, Jan de Lange, and Martin van Reeuwijk. It was adapted for use in American schools by Mary S. Spence and Jonathan Brendefur.

National Center for Research in Mathematical Sciences Education Staff

Thomas A. Romberg
Director

Joan Daniels Pedro
Assistant to the Director

Gail Burrill
Coordinator
Field Test Materials

Margaret R. Meyer
Coordinator
Pilot Test Materials

Mary Ann Fix
Editorial Coordinator

Sherian Foster
Editorial Coordinator

James A. Middleton
Pilot Test Coordinator

Project Staff

Jonathan Brendefur
Laura J. Brinker
James Browne
Jack Burrill
Rose Byrd
Peter Christiansen
Barbara Clarke
Doug Clarke
Beth R. Cole

Fae Dremock
Jasmina Milinkovic
Margaret A. Pligge
Mary C. Shafer
Julia A. Shew
Aaron N. Simon
Marvin Smith
Stephanie Z. Smith
Mary S. Spence

Freudenthal Institute Staff

Jan de Lange
Director

Els Feijs
Coordinator

Martin van Reeuwijk
Coordinator

Project Staff

Mieke Abels
Nina Boswinkel
Frans van Galen
Koeno Gravemeijer
Marja van den Heuvel-Panhuizen
Jan Auke de Jong
Vincent Jonker
Ronald Keijzer

Martin Kindt
Jansie Niehaus
Nanda Querelle
Anton Roodhardt
Leen Streefland
Adri Treffers
Monica Wijers
Astrid de Wild

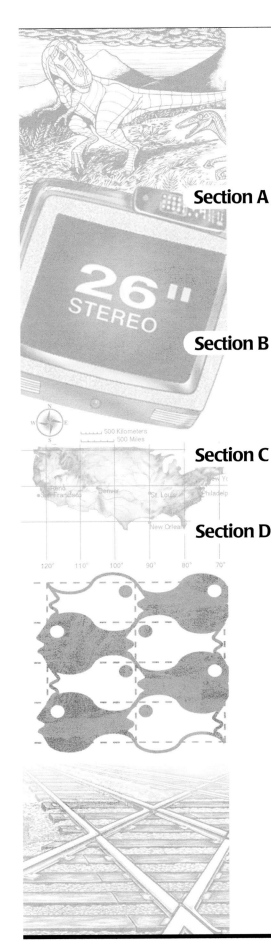

Table of Contents

Dear Student,

Welcome to *Looking at an Angle*.

In this unit you will learn about vision lines and blind areas. Have you ever been on one of the top floors of a tall office or apartment building? When you looked out the window, were you able to see the sidewalk directly below the building? If you could see the sidewalk, it was in your field of vision; if you could not see the sidewalk, it was in your blind spot.

The relationship between vision lines and light rays and the relationship between blind spots and shadows are some of the topics that you will explore in this unit. Have you ever noticed how the length of a shadow varies according to the time of day? As part of an activity, you will measure the length of the shadow of a stick and the corresponding angle of the sun at different times of the day. You will then determine how the angle of the sun affects the length of a shadow.

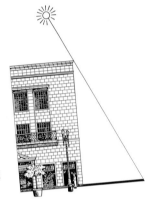

Besides looking at the angle of the sun, you will also study the angle that a ladder makes with the floor when it is leaning against a wall and the angle that a descending hang glider makes with the ground. You will learn two different ways to identify the steepness of an object: the angle the object makes with the ground and the tangent of that angle.

We hope you enjoy discovering the many ways of "looking at an angle."

Sincerely,

The Mathematics in Context Development Team

A. NOW YOU SEE IT, NOW YOU DON'T

The Grand Canyon

The Grand Canyon is one of the most famous natural wonders of the world. It is a huge gorge, cut by the Colorado River into the high plateau of northwestern Arizona. The total length of the gorge is 446 kilometers. Approximately 90 kilometers of the gorge are located in Grand Canyon National Park. The north rim of the canyon (the Kaibab Plateau) is about 2,500 meters above sea level.

The above photo shows part of the Colorado River. You can see the river on the left side of the photo.

1. Why can't you see the continuation of the river on the lower right side of the photo?

In fact, the Colorado River can barely be seen from most viewpoints in Grand Canyon National Park.

The picture on the right shows a hiker on the north rim overlooking a portion of the canyon.

2. Can the hiker see the river directly below her? Explain.

Shown below are a photograph and a drawing of the same area of the Grand Canyon. From the drawing, you can see that the canyon walls are shaped like stairs.

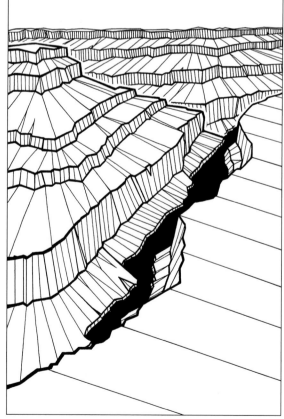

3. What other differences do you notice between the photo and the drawing?

Activity

The Table Canyon Model

In this activity, you will build your own "table canyon" to investigate how much of the "river" can be seen from different perspectives.

i. Place two tables parallel to each other, with enough room between them for another table to fit.

ii. Hang large sheets of paper from the tables to the floor as shown in the drawing on the right. (The paper represents the canyon walls, and the floor between the two tables represents the river.)

iii. Sit behind one of the tables, and have another student sit behind the other.

iv. Have a third student make at least three marks on each canyon wall to show the lowest place visible to each of you.

4. a. Can either of you see the river below? Explain.

   b. On which wall are the marks the highest? Explain.

   c. Are all the marks on one wall the same height? Explain.

5. Describe some possible changes that would allow you to see the river. How does each change affect what you can see?

6. a. If there were a boat on the river, where could the boat be located so that both of you can see it?

   b. What would happen if the boat moves closer to one of the canyon walls?

7. Write a report on this activity describing your investigations and discoveries. You may want to use the terms *visible, not visible,* and *blind spot* in your report.

Activity

The Paper Canyon Model

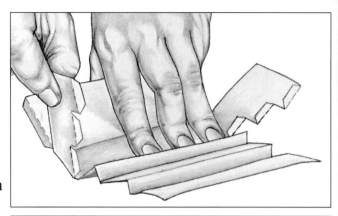

In this activity, you will build a simplified paper model of part of a canyon, as shown on the right. This model can help you to explain why it is sometimes difficult to see the river from different locations on the rim of a canyon.

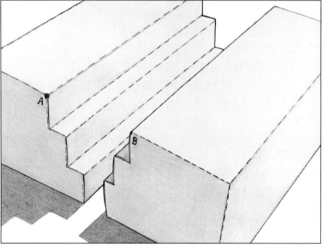

i. Cut out the nets on **Student Activity Sheets 1** and **2.**

ii. Fold the nets along the dotted lines and then tape the sides of each net to make two canyon walls.

iii. Place the canyon walls so that they face each other as shown in the picture on the right.

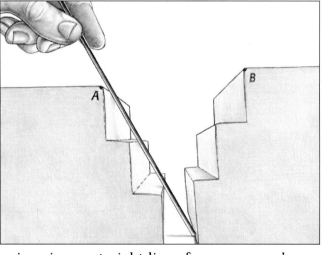

With this model, you can construct vision lines with a thin, straight object, such as a straw. *Vision lines* are imaginary, straight lines from a person's eyes to an object that show what is in the person's field of vision.

The following drawing shows a side view of the paper canyon model that you built on page 4.

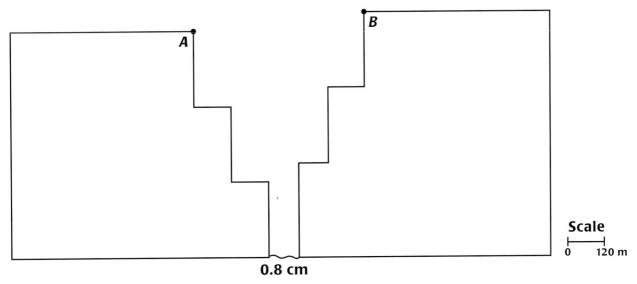

0.8 cm

Scale
0   120 m

To answer problems **8–12,** use either the model you made in the previous activity and a straw or use **Student Activity Sheet 3** and a straightedge. If you use your paper model, be sure to place the canyon walls as shown above, leaving a space of 0.8 centimeter for the river.

8. Is it possible to see the river from point *A* on the left rim? Why or why not?

9. What is the actual height of the left canyon wall represented by the above scale model?

10. What is the actual width of the river represented by the above scale model?

11. If the river were 1.2 centimeters wide in the above scale model, could it be seen from point *A*? Explain.

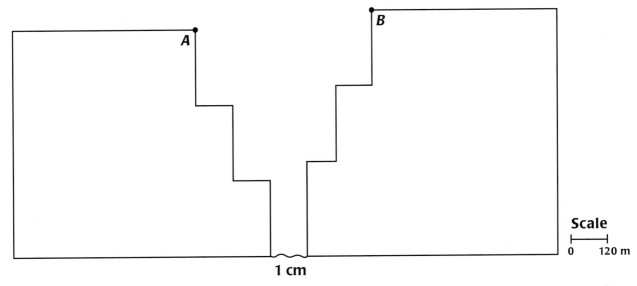

1 cm

Scale
0   120 m

12. In the above drawing, the river is 1 centimeter wide. Is it possible to see the river from point *B*? If not, which ledge is blocking your view? Explain.

Most of the ledges of the Grand Canyon are rather wide.

13. Explain why wide canyon ledges make it difficult to see the river.

Activity

In the following activity, you will create a canyon model with a curve by building extensions for the model you made on page 4.

i. Cut out the nets on **Student Activity Sheets 4** and **5**. Fold the nets along the dotted lines and then tape the sides together to create two canyon walls.

ii. Place extension A next to the canyon wall on the left that is labeled with point *A*. Place extension B next to the canyon wall on the right that is labeled with point *B*.

In this expanded model, there are some good places to view the river.

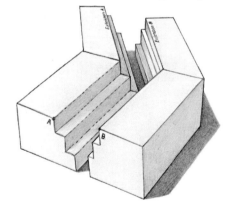

14. Make a sketch of the model shown above. On your sketch, indicate the best places on the canyon rim for viewing the river. Use arrows to show the direction in which the river is visible.

SHIPS AHOY

Picture yourself in a small rowboat rowing toward a ship that is tied to a dock. In the first picture, the captain at the helm of the ship is able to see you. As you get closer, at some point the captain is no longer able to see you.

15. Explain why the captain probably cannot see you in the last picture at the bottom of the page.

Closer

Closer

Closer

The shape of the ship and the captain's height and position in the ship determine what the captain can and cannot see in front of the ship. To find the captain's field of vision, you can draw a vision line (a line that extends from the captain's eyes, over the edge of the ship, and to the water).

16. For each ship shown on **Student Activity Sheet 6,** draw a vision line from the captain, over the front edge of the ship, to the water. Measure the angle between the vision line and the water. (The captain is located at the star symbol.)

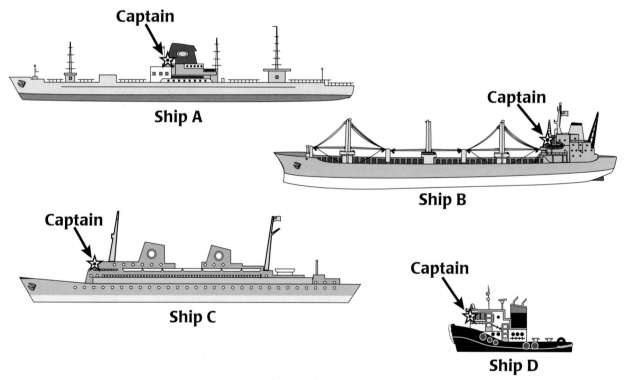

17. Compare the ships on **Student Activity Sheet 6.**

   a. On which ship is the captain's blind area the smallest? Explain.

   b. How does the shape of the ship affect the captain's view?

   c. How does the angle between the vision line and the water affect the captain's view?

Vision lines, such as the ones you drew on **Student Activity Sheet 6,** do not show everything that captains can and cannot see. For example, some ships' bridges, the area from which the captain navigates the ship, are specially constructed to improve the captain's view. The captain can walk across the bridge, from one side of the boat to the other side, to increase his or her field of vision.

On the left is a picture of the *Queen Elizabeth II.* Notice how the bridge, located between the arrows, has wings that project out on each side of the ship.

18. Explain how the wings of the bridge give the captain a better view of the water in front of the ship.

Hydrofoils have fins that raise the boat out of the water when it travels at high speeds.

19. Make two side-view drawings of a hydrofoil: one of the hydrofoil in the water traveling at a slow speed and one of it raised out of the water traveling at a high speed. Use vision lines to show the difference between the captain's view in each drawing. (You may design your own hydrofoil.)

Photo 1

Photo 2

The above photos show what a passenger in a boat can see at different speeds. In photo 1, the boat is moving slowly. In photo 2, the boat is moving more quickly.

20. Make side-view drawings of the boat for each photo. Be sure to draw vision lines and indicate the area of the water that the passenger cannot see. Explain the differences in the two views.

Suppose that you are swimming in the water and a large boat is coming toward you. If you are too close to the boat, the captain may not be able to see you! In order to see a larger area of the water, a captain may travel in a zigzag course, as shown in the picture below.

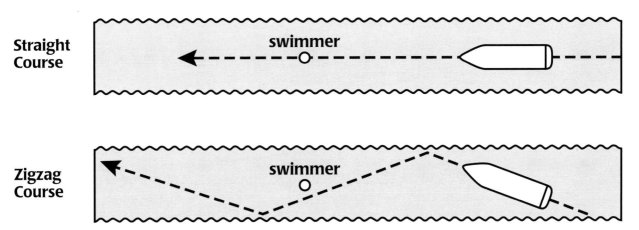

21. Explain why the captain has a better chance of seeing something in front of the boat by traveling in a zigzag course.

Activity

For this activity, each group of students needs a piece of string and a toy boat. The boat can be made of either plastic or wood, but it must have a flat bottom.

Line up all the boats in the front of the classroom. For each boat, assign a number and determine the captain's location.

22. Without measuring, decide which boat has the largest blind spot and which has the smallest blind spot. Explain your decisions.

When comparing blind spots, you have to take into account the size of the boat. A large boat will probably have a large blind spot, but you must consider the size of the blind spot relative to the size of the boat.

23. In your group, use the following method to measure your boat's blind spot:

   i. Place your boat on the grid on **Student Activity Sheet 7.** Trace the bottom of the boat. Attach a piece of string to the boat at the place where the captain is located. (The string represents the captain's vision line.)

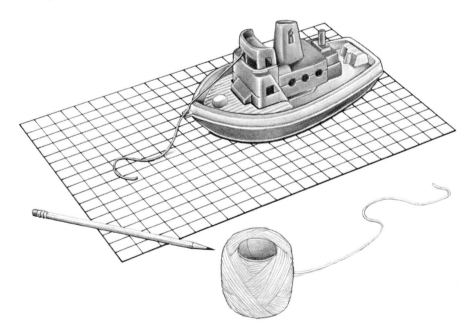

ii. Using the string and a pencil, mark the spot on the grid where the captain's vision line hits the water. Make sure the vision line is taut and touches the edge of the boat.

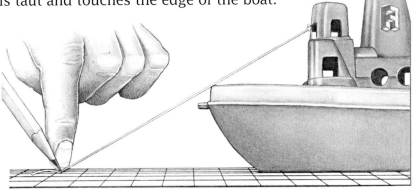

iii. Mark several places on the grid where the captain's vision line hits the water, so that you can determine the shape of the blind spot (the captain looks straight ahead and sideways). If the grid paper is not large enough, tape several pieces together. Draw the blind spot on the grid paper.

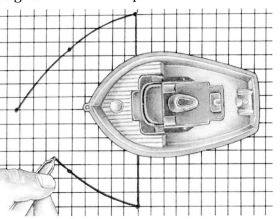

iv. Find the area of the blind spot. (*Note:* Each square of the grid is one square centimeter.)

24. Make a list of the data for each boat. Decide which boat has the largest blind spot relative to its size and which has the smallest blind spot relative to its size.

Activity

In this activity, you will investigate the blind area of a tugboat.

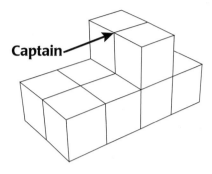

Captain

i. Build a model of the tugboat shown on the left with 1-centimeter blocks.

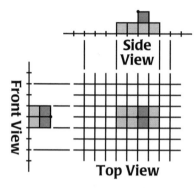

Side View

Front View

Top View

ii. Place your boat on the top-view outline of the tugboat on **Student Activity Sheet 8.**

iii. Use string to represent the captain's vision line.

25. a. On **Student Activity Sheet 8,** draw the captain's vision lines for the side, top, and front views.

b. In the top view, shade the area of the grid that represents the blind area of the boat.

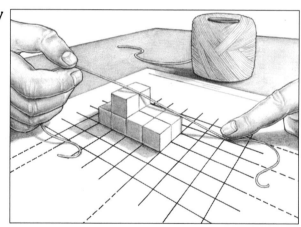

26. On **Student Activity Sheet 9,** draw vision lines and shade the blind area for the view shown. (One vision line has already been drawn.)

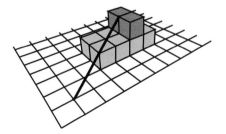

Cars and Blind Spots

The above photograph is of a 1958 Pontiac Star Chief. This car is 5.25 meters long. Shown below is a side view of the car with vision lines indicating the blind area.

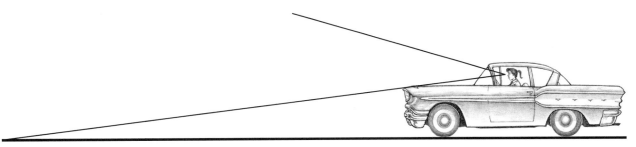

Today, cars are designed so that the blind area in front of the car is much smaller. The car shown below is a 1997 Buick Skylark that is 4.7 meters long. Notice how the vision line touches the hood of this car.

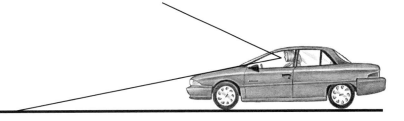

27. Find the length of road in front of each car that cannot be seen by the driver.

28. Which car has the longest relative blind spot?

29. What does the vision line that extends upward from each car indicate? Why is it important that this vision line be as close to vertical as possible?

Summary

When an object is hidden from your view because something is in the way, the area that you cannot see is called the *blind area* or *blind spot.*

Vision lines are imaginary lines that go from a person's eyes to an object. Vision lines show what is in a person's line of sight, and they can be used to determine whether or not an object is visible.

In this section, you used vision lines to discover that the Colorado River is not visible in some parts of the Grand Canyon. You also used vision lines to find the captain's blind area for ships of various sizes.

Summary Questions

30. Describe a situation from your daily life which involves a blind spot. Include a picture of the situation with the blind spot clearly indicated.

Hide and See

"Hide and See" is a game played by two teams, a red team and a blue team. The red team is positioned at the fort. The blue team is trying to approach the fort without being seen.

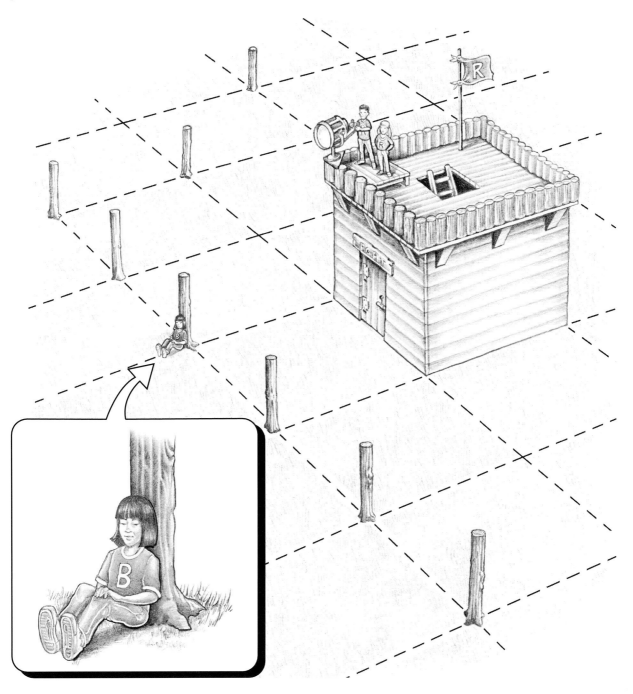

Regina, a member of the blue team, approaches the fort without being seen. She then sits behind a tree stump, unseen from the fort, as shown in the above picture.

1. Explain why the red team members on top of the fort cannot see Regina.

The leader of the blue team advises her team members to take similar positions behind the other tree stumps, so that they cannot be seen from the fort.

The following picture shows how she places her team members.

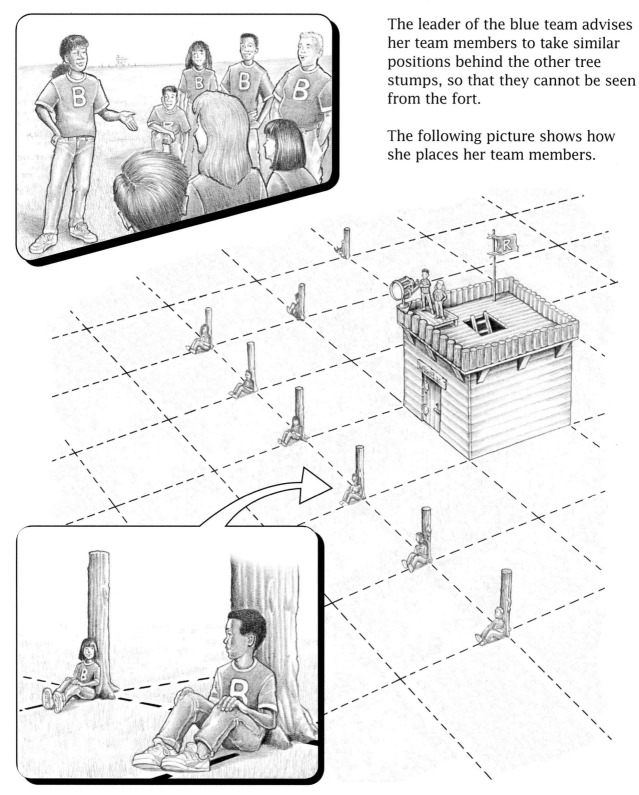

2. Can the members of the red team on top of the fort see any members of the blue team who are positioned behind the tree stumps? Explain.

3. Explain how each member of the blue team should sit so that they cannot be seen from the top of the fort. Include a sketch with your explanation.

The blue team members still are not quite sure how to position themselves behind the tree stumps without being seen. Regina has an idea. She suggests that they wait until night when the searchlight at the fort is turned on. She says, "We have to place all our team members in the shadows of the tree stumps made by the searchlight."

4. How will the searchlight help the blue team figure out how to sit behind the tree stumps without being seen?

The following pictures show the shadows made by the searchlight for two tree stumps. One picture is drawn using a perspective projection, the other is drawn using a parallel projection.

Nighttime Perspective Projection

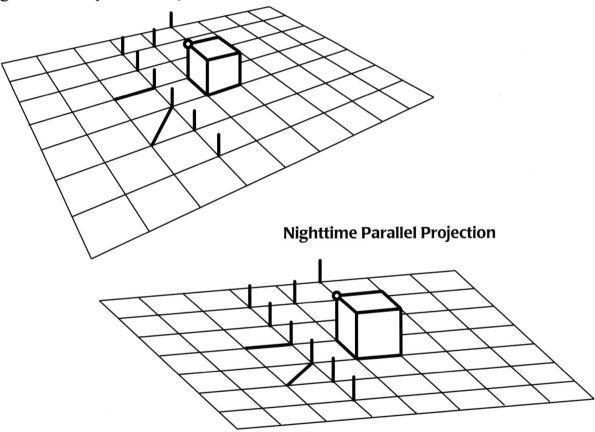

Nighttime Parallel Projection

5. Explain at least two differences between each projection.

6. On **Student Activity Sheet 10,** draw the shadows of the other tree stumps for each projection.

For problem **6,** you made approximate drawings of the shadows of the tree stumps. However, to make a precise drawing of the shadows you need to know the following:

- the direction of the shadows, and

- the length of the shadows.

A side view and a top view of the shadows can help you to make a precise drawing.

Side View

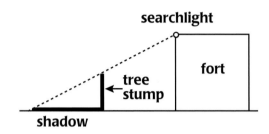

Top View

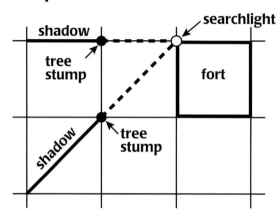

In the above drawings, the tree stump is half as high as the fort. The searchlight is at the top left corner of the fort.

7. How can the above pictures help you to make a precise drawing of the shadows?

8. On **Student Activity Sheet 11,** the shadows of two tree stumps have already been drawn in a picture of the top view of the fort and tree stumps.

a. Draw the shadows of the other tree stumps.

b. Explain how you found the directions and lengths for the shadows you drew.

Nighttime Top View

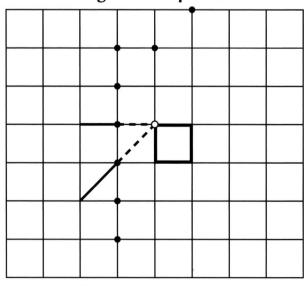

Now back to the game "Hide and See." At night, the red team turns on the fort's searchlight. All the blue team members are sitting in the shadows of the tree stumps and cannot be seen from the fort.

At daybreak, the shadows of the tree stumps are caused by the sun, not the searchlight. The shadows have changed, so now the blue team members can be easily seen by the red team members on top of the fort.

Daytime Perspective Projection

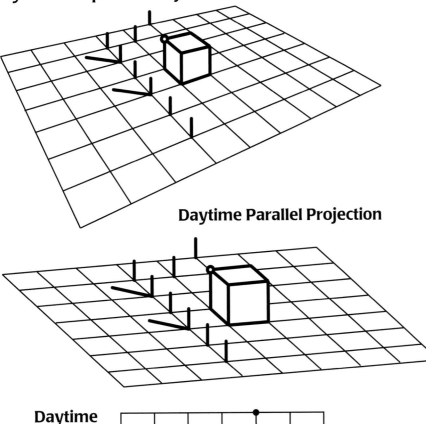

Daytime Parallel Projection

Daytime Top View

In the three pictures shown on the left, the shadows of two tree stumps caused by the sun have been drawn.

9. Draw the shadows of the other tree stumps on **Student Activity Sheet 12.**

10. Explain the differences between the shadows caused by the searchlight at night and the shadows caused by the sun during the day.

11. Draw the shadow of the fort in the top view on **Student Activity Sheet 12.** (*Note:* The fort is twice as tall as the tree stumps.)

Shadows and the Sun

The sun causes parallel objects to cast parallel shadows. For example, the bars of the railing in the photograph on the right cast parallel shadows on the sidewalk.

Activity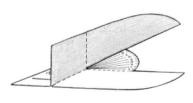

In this activity, you will go outside on a sunny day to investigate the shadows caused by the sun.

First, you need to assemble your angle measure tool (AMT). Cut out the figure on **Student Activity Sheet 13** along the solid lines. Make the first fold as shown below and glue the matching shaded pieces together. Continue to fold your AMT in the order shown below.

Fold 1

Fold 2

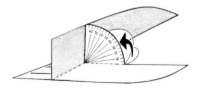

Fold 3

Fold 4

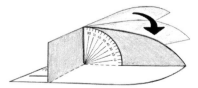

For your activity, you will need the following items:

- a stick about 1.2 meters long
- a stick about 0.7 meter long
- a centimeter tape measure
- several meters of string
- your AMT
- a directional compass

Put both sticks into the ground, about 2 meters apart. The longer stick should have a height of 1 meter above the ground, and the shorter stick should have a height of 0.5 meter above the ground. The sticks should be perfectly vertical.

12. In your notebook, copy the following table. Measure at least five different times during the day and fill in your table. (Add more blank rows to your table as needed.)

| Time of Day | Direction of Sun | 0.5-meter Stick | | 1-meter Stick | |
		Length of Shadow (in cm)	Angle of Sun's Rays	Length of Shadow (in cm)	Angle of Sun's Rays

Use your compass to determine the direction from which the sun is shining. Use your tape measure to measure the lengths of the shadows of both sticks, and use your AMT and string (as shown below) to measure the angle between the sun's rays and the ground for both sticks. Be sure to stretch the string to where the shadow ends and place your AMT there.

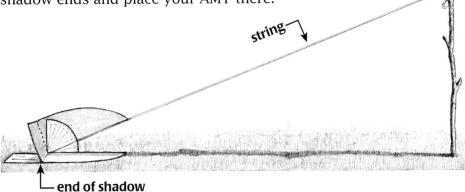

string

end of shadow

Use your data from the table in problem **12** to answer the following problems:

13. a. Describe the movement of the sun during the day.

b. Describe how the directions of the shadows change during the day. How are the shadows related to the direction from which the sun is shining?

c. Describe the changes in the lengths of the shadows during the day. When are the shadows the longest, and when are they the shortest?

14. a. Compare the shadows of the longer stick with the shadows of the shorter stick. Describe the relationship between the length of the shadow and the height of the stick.

b. Were the shadows of the two sticks parallel at all times? Explain.

15. a. Compare the angle of the sun's rays for each stick at any moment during the day.

b. Describe how the angle of the sun's rays changed during the day. When is the angle the largest, and when is it the smallest?

c. How is the size of the angle of the sun's rays related to the length of the shadows?

The picture below shows the shadows of two buildings at noon. The sun is shining from the south. One building is twice as tall as the other.

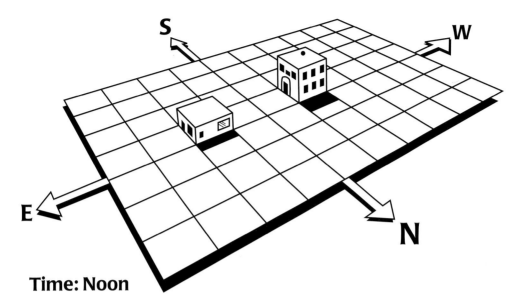

Time: Noon

16. Study the shadows of the buildings shown above. Describe the directions and the lengths of the shadows.

In the four pictures below, you see the two buildings at different times of day.

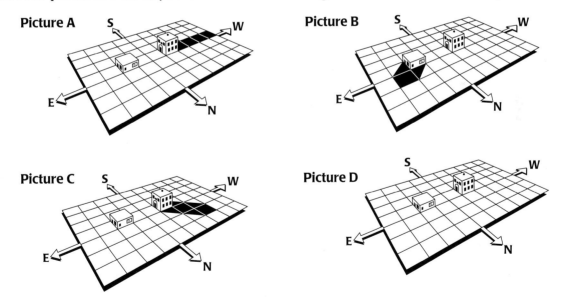

17. a. On **Student Activity Sheet 14,** draw in the shadows that are missing. (*Note:* Picture D needs both shadows drawn in.)

b. Label each picture with an appropriate time of day.

18. Describe how the lengths of the shadows change during the day. Make drawings or graphs to illustrate your descriptions.

The lower the sun is, the longer the shadows that are cast. The height of the sun not only depends on the time of the day, but also on the season. Shown below is a side view of a building around noon during the summer.

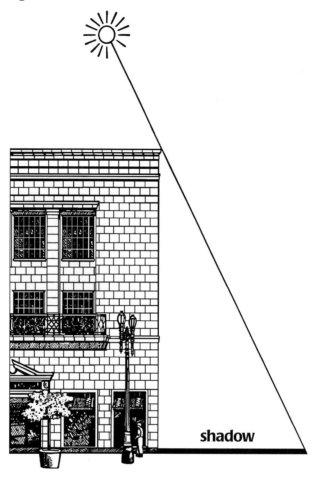

shadow

The length of the above building's shadow is one-half the height of the building.

19. Measure the angle between the sun's rays and the ground.

Around noon during the winter, the length of this building's shadow is $2\frac{1}{2}$ times the height of the building.

20. a. Draw a side view of the building and its shadow around noon during the winter.

   b. Measure the angle between the sun's rays and the ground.

Around noon during the spring, the angle between the sun's rays and the ground is 45°.

21. a. Draw a side view of the building and its shadow around noon during the spring.

   b. If the building is 40 meters tall, how long is its shadow?

22. Describe the changes in the length of the shadow and the angle of the sun's rays from season to season.

Shadows and a Light

Now back to the game "Hide and See." Recall that the shadows cast by the fort's searchlight during the night were different than those cast by the sun during the day.

Suppose that the blue team builds a wall between the two tree stumps directly in front of the fort. The wall is the same height as the tree stumps.

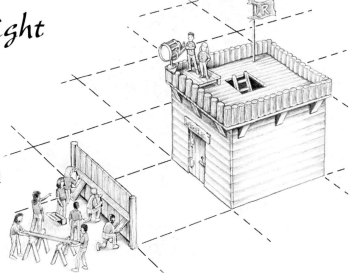

The following picture shows the shadow of the wall when the searchlight is on.

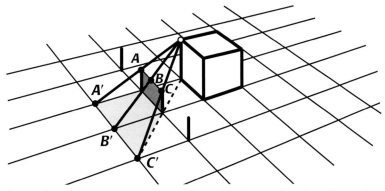

Point *A'* is the shadow of point *A*, point *B'* is the shadow of point *B*, and point *C'* is the shadow of point *C*.

The red team decides to move the searchlight to the other front corner of the fort.

23. a. On **Student Activity Sheet 15,** draw the shadow of the wall caused by placing the searchlight on the other front corner of the fort.

b. Does moving the searchlight from one front corner of the fort to the other change the area of the shadow? Explain.

Suppose the wall is placed twice as far from the fort as shown on the right. The leader of the blue team thinks that this will make the area of the shadow caused by the searchlight twice as big, thus allowing more room for the blue team to hide.

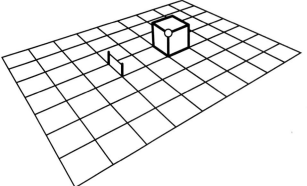

24. Is the leader of the blue team correct? Explain. (You might want to make a top-view drawing to find your answer.)

Summary

Shadows are similar to blind spots (or blind areas). Shadows can be caused by two kinds of light:

- light that is nearby, such as a streetlight
- light that is very far away, such as the sun

When light comes from a nearby point, shadows are cast in different directions. When light comes from a far away source, the light rays are parallel, and the shadows are also parallel.

Summary Questions

25. Describe what a shadow is. How are shadows and blind spots similar?

In the picture on the right, you see a streetlight surrounded by posts.

26. On **Student Activity Sheet 16,** draw in the missing shadows. In top view A, it is nighttime, and the streetlight is on. In top view B, it is daytime, the streetlight is off, and the sun is shining.

Top View A   **Top View B**

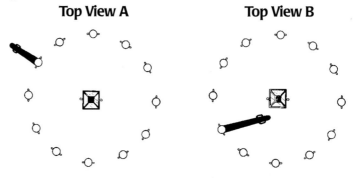

C. SHADOWS AND ANGLES

Acoma Pueblo

The Acoma Pueblo is considered the oldest continually inhabited village in the United States. The above drawing is of the Acoma Pueblo as it might have looked over 100 years ago. Located near Albuquerque, New Mexico, it is famous for its beautiful pottery and architecture. By analyzing the pottery, archaeologists have determined that this village was settled about 1,000 years ago.

The photograph on the left shows the typical architecture of a main street of the village. This picture was taken in the morning.

1. Describe how the shadows will be different at noon.

Originally, the houses in the Acoma Pueblo had no front doors; ladders were used to enter the houses on the second floor. Ladders propped against the houses formed different angles. The steepness of the ladders can be measured several ways.

Recall from Section B that the sun's rays are parallel. The drawing below shows a ladder and its shadow. The drawing also shows how the sun casts a shadow for one rung of the ladder.

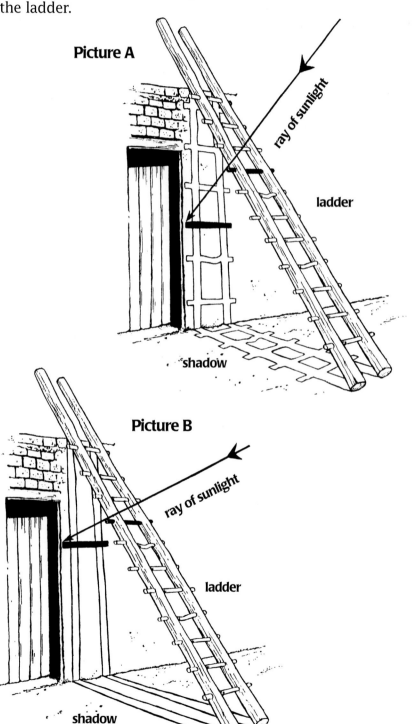

Picture A

ray of sunlight

ladder

shadow

Picture B

ray of sunlight

ladder

shadow

2. On picture A on **Student Activity Sheet 17,** draw a ray of sunlight that casts a shadow for each of the other 10 rungs.

The drawing on the left shows the same ladder in the same position, but at a different time of day.

3. On picture B on **Student Activity Sheet 17,** draw a ray of sunlight and the corresponding shadow for each of the other 10 rungs.

The following drawings show two side views of the same ladder leaning against a wall.

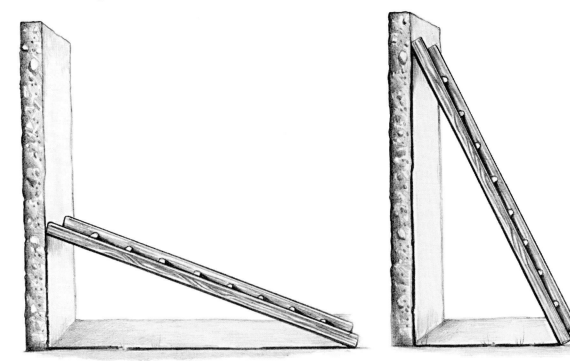

4. Describe the differences between the ways the ladder is positioned against the wall in the above drawings.

5. a. What problems might occur if the ladder is very steep?

  b. What problems might occur if the ladder is not steep enough?

As the steepness of the ladder changes, the following measures also change:

- the height on the wall that can be reached by the top of the ladder,
- the distance between the foot of the ladder and the wall,
- the angle between the ladder and the ground.

6. Investigate different levels of steepness by using a ruler or pencil to represent a ladder and an upright book or box to represent a wall. Describe your discoveries. (You may use drawings.)

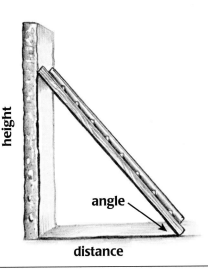

On the right is a drawing of a ladder leaning against a wall. Angles are often given names. Sometimes the name of the angle is a letter of the Greek alphabet. The first letter in the Greek alphabet is α (*alpha*), the second letter is β (*beta*), and the third letter is γ (*gamma*).

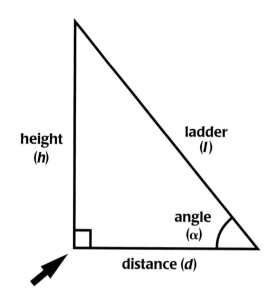

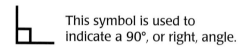 This symbol is used to indicate a 90°, or right, angle.

7. Why must the angle between the height (*h*) and the distance (*d*) be 90°?

8. Measure the angle α for the ladder in the above drawing.

There are several ways to measure the steepness of a ladder. You can measure the angle α, or you can find the ratio of the height to the distance. The ratio of the height to the distance can be expressed as a fraction or a decimal.

9. What happens to the angle α as the ratio of the height to the distance increases?

10. Use a compass card or a protractor and a ruler to make side-view drawings to scale of a ladder leaning against a wall for each of the following situations. Also, label α, *h*, and *d* with their measures, and find the height-to-distance ratio.

　a. α = 45°

　b. *h* = 2, *d* = 1

　c. α = 30°

　d. *h* = 1, *d* = 2

　e. α = 60°

11. Copy the following table and fill it in using your data from problem **10.** Arrange your entries so that the angle measures increase from left to right.

Steepness Table

α (angle measure in degrees)					
h:d (ratio of height to distance)					

12. Use the table from problem **11** to make a graph of the height-to-distance ratio for a ladder leaning against a wall. Label your graph as shown below.

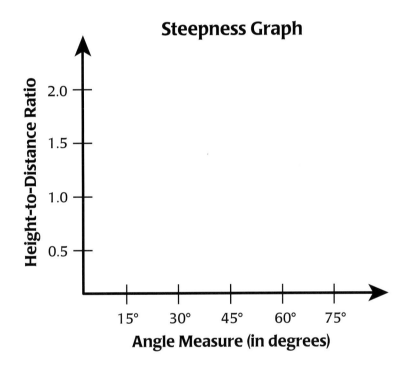

13. Explain the information shown in your graph. Compare your graph to your answer to problem **9.**

Suppose that it is safe to be on a ladder when the ratio $h:d$ is larger than two and smaller than three.

14. Give a range of angles at which a ladder can be positioned safely.

Summary

As the angle between a ladder and the ground increases, the height of the wall that can be reached by the top of the ladder increases. At the same time, the distance between the foot of the ladder and the wall decreases.

In the same way, as the angle between a ray of sunlight and the ground increases, a shadow on the ground becomes shorter.

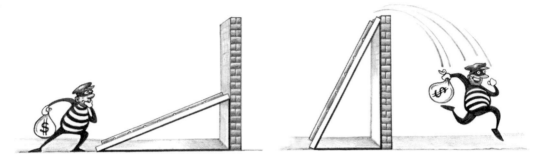

The steepness of a ladder can be measured in the following two ways:

• by the angle (the larger the angle, the steeper the ladder),

• by the ratio of the height to the distance, or *h:d* (the larger the ratio, the steeper the ladder).

Summary Questions

Recall the model of the canyon from Section A. The drawing on the right is a cross-section of another canyon model. The numbers indicate the scale of the height and the width of the ledges and the width of the river.

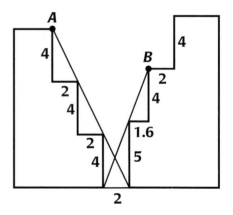

15. Which vision line is steeper: the one from point *A* down to the river or the one from point *B* down to the river? Support your answer with information about the angle between the vision line and the river, and the ratio of the height to the distance.

HANG GLIDERS

Hang gliders are light, kite-like gliders that carry a pilot in a harness. The pilot takes off from a hill or a cliff against the wind. The hang glider then slowly descends to the ground.

When pilots make their first flight with a new glider, they are very careful because they do not know how quickly the glider will descend.

Marianne, the pilot in the above picture, decides to make her first jump from a 10-meter-high cliff. She glides along a straight line, covering 40 meters of ground.

Shown below is a picture of Marianne's first flight path.

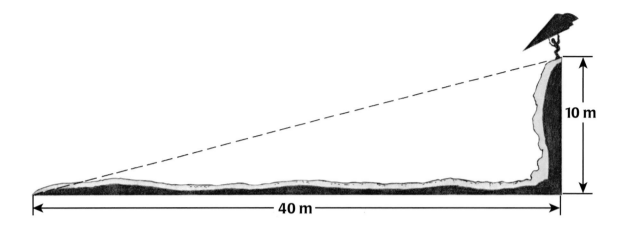

After several successful flights, she decides to go to a higher cliff. This cliff is 15 meters high.

1. How much ground distance does the glider cover from the higher cliff? (*Note:* Assume that the steepness of the flight path remains the same.)

2. Marianne makes flights from three cliffs that are 20 meters, 50 meters, and 100 meters high. How much ground distance does the glider cover on each flight?

Marianne has designed a glider that can travel farther than her first one. With the new glider, Marianne claims, "When jumping from a 10-meter-high cliff, I can cover 70 meters of ground!"

3. a. Draw a side view of Marianne's flight path with the new glider.

b. Copy the table below and complete it for the new glider.

Height (in meters)	10	25	100			
Distance (in meters)	70			245	1,000	

The above picture is based on three separate photographs, taken one after the other. It shows a model glider that is used in laboratory experiments. By taking three pictures within a short period of time, you can clearly see the path of the glider.

4. In your notebook, trace the path of the above glider and make a scale drawing, similar to the drawing on top of page 36, of its possible flight path to answer the following questions:

   a. If the glider in the picture is launched from a height of 5 meters, how far will the glider fly before landing?

   b. How far will the glider fly from a 10-meter cliff?

   c. Compare the distances covered by Marianne's two hang gliders and this model glider. If all three are launched from 10 meters, which one flies the farthest? Explain.

Activity

Make paper airplanes and have a contest to find out whose plane flies the farthest. (You might want to make a rule that all planes must fly in a fairly straight path; it is hard to measure a plane's distance when it flies in circles!)

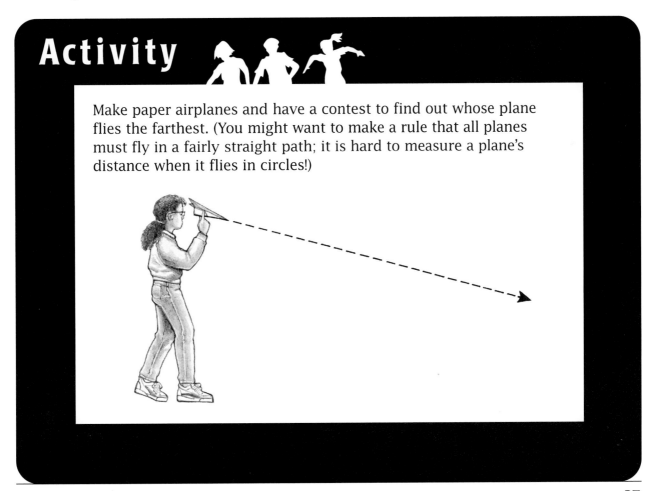

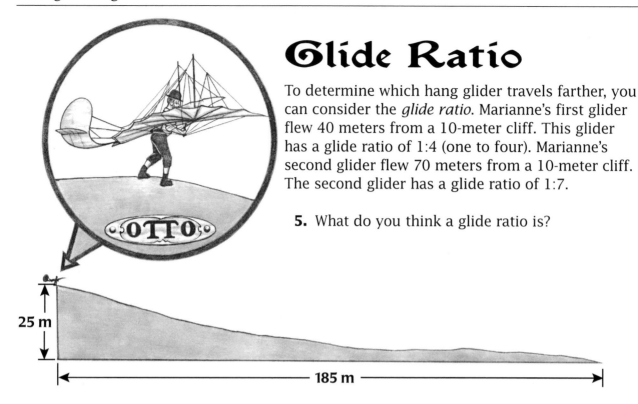

Glide Ratio

To determine which hang glider travels farther, you can consider the *glide ratio*. Marianne's first glider flew 40 meters from a 10-meter cliff. This glider has a glide ratio of 1:4 (one to four). Marianne's second glider flew 70 meters from a 10-meter cliff. The second glider has a glide ratio of 1:7.

5. What do you think a glide ratio is?

25 m

185 m

Otto Lilienthal made more than 2,000 flights with hang gliders at the end of the 19th century. Suppose that on one of his flights from the Rhinower Hills near Berlin, Germany, he started from a height of 25 meters and covered 185 meters of ground distance as shown above. On his next flight, suppose he redesigned his glider a bit, started from a height of 20 meters, and traveled a distance of 155 meters along the ground.

6. What are the glide ratios of Otto's two gliders? Which glider can travel farther?

7. Suppose that a glider has a glide ratio of 1:8. It takes off from a cliff and covers 120 meters of ground distance. How high is the cliff?

8. Make scale drawings to represent the following glide ratios:

    a. 1:1   **b.** 1:2   **c.** 1:4

    d. 1:10   **e.** 1:20

In Section C when you studied ladders at different angles, you made a table similar to the one below showing the angle between the ladder and the ground, and the ratio of the height to the distance.

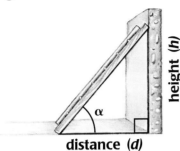

Ladder Steepness

α	27°	30°	45°	60°	63°
h:d	0.5	0.6	1	1.7	2

You can organize your information about the steepness of the glide path of a hang glider with a similar table. The angle that the hang glider makes with the ground as it descends is called a *glide angle*.

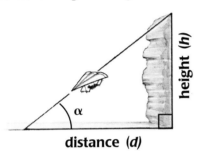

Glide Path Steepness

Glide Angle α					
Glide Ratio h:d	1:1	1:2	1:4	1:10	1:20

9. Copy the above table into your notebook. Fill in the missing glide angles by measuring the angles in each of the scale drawings you made for problem **8** with a protractor.

Glide ratios can also be expressed as fractions or decimals.

10. Which of the following glide ratios are equivalent?

1:25	$\frac{4}{100}$	1:20	3:75	$\frac{1}{20}$
$\frac{1}{30}$	2:40	0.04	$\frac{1}{25}$	4:100
0.05	$\frac{1}{4}$	0.20	4:120	$\frac{2}{50}$

11. In your notebook, graph the information from the table in problem **9.** Label the axes as shown on the right, and take care to be precise when making a scale for the axes.

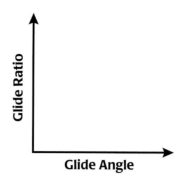

12. Explain what your graph shows.

Suppose that it is safe to fly gliders that have a glide ratio smaller than 1:10.

13. What is the largest glide angle that is safe?

14. Suppose three gliders have the following glide ratios:

- Glider 1   1:27
- Glider 2   0.04
- Glider 3 $\frac{3}{78}$

Which glider is the safest? Explain.

From Glide Ratio to Tangent

The relationship between the glide ratio and the glide angle is very important in hang gliding as well as in other applications, such as the placement of a ladder. For this reason, there are several ways to express this ratio and angle.

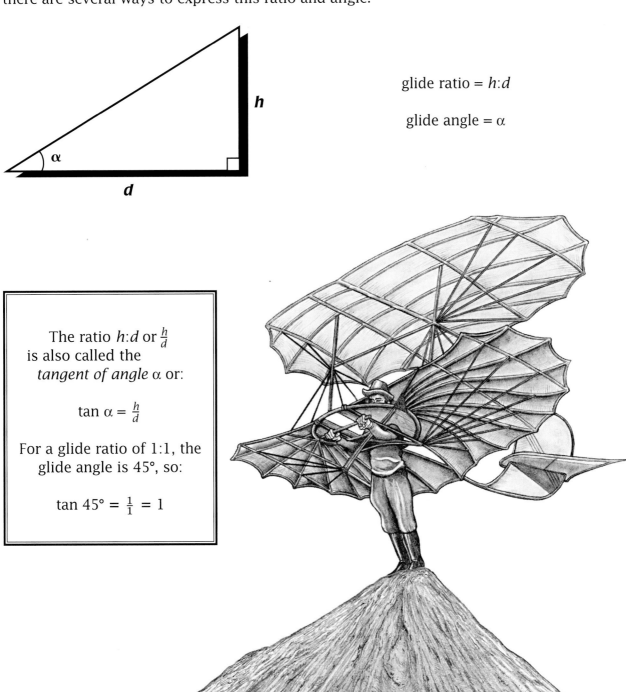

glide ratio = $h{:}d$

glide angle = α

The ratio $h{:}d$ or $\frac{h}{d}$ is also called the *tangent of angle* α or:

$$\tan \alpha = \frac{h}{d}$$

For a glide ratio of 1:1, the glide angle is 45°, so:

$$\tan 45° = \frac{1}{1} = 1$$

Suppose that another one of Otto's hang gliders, shown above, has a glide ratio of 1:7. This means that the tangent of the glide angle is 1 to 7 (or $\frac{1}{7}$).

A Matter of Notation

Suppose that a glider follows the flight path shown on the right.

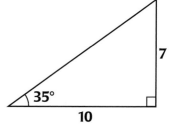

From this information, you can say that the glide ratio of a 35° angle is 0.7 (or 7:10). You can also write this information in the following way:

$$\tan 35° = \frac{7}{10} = 0.7$$

For the situation shown on the right, you can state the following:

$$\tan A = \frac{25}{53} \approx 0.47$$

15. Complete the statements below for each of the following triangles:

a.

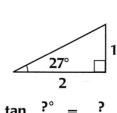

$\tan \underline{\ ?\ }° = \underline{\ ?\ }$

b.

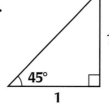

$\tan \underline{\ ?\ }° = \underline{\ ?\ }$

c.

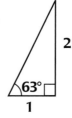

$\tan \underline{\ ?\ }° = \underline{\ ?\ }$

d.

$\tan \underline{\ ?\ }° = \underline{\ ?\ }$

Peter wants to buy a balsa wood flyer for his nephew, but he is not sure which flyer to buy. The salesperson at the hobby store claims, "The smaller the tangent of the glide angle, the better the glider."

16. Is the salesperson correct? Explain.

17. Suppose for triangle *ABC*, the measure of angle *B* is 90° and $\tan A = \frac{3}{5}$.

   a. Make a scale drawing of triangle *ABC*.

   b. If you drew triangle *ABC* so that side *AB* measures 10 centimeters, what would be the length of side *BC*?

   c. What is the measure of angle *A* in triangle *ABC*?

The following table lists some angles and the approximate measures of their tangents.

Angle	0°	1°	2°	3°	4°	5°	31°	32°	33°	34°	35°
Tangent	0	0.02	0.04	0.05	0.07	0.09	0.60	0.63	0.65	0.68	0.70

Use the above table to answer the following problems:

18. **a.** Draw a side view of the flight path for a glider whose glide angle is 5°.

   b. What is the glide ratio for this glider?

19. If the glide angle is 35°, how much ground distance does a glider cover from a height of 100 meters?

20. If a ladder makes an 80° angle with the ground, what can you determine about the position of the ladder from the information that tan 80° equals about 5.7?

Angle (in degrees)	Tangent
0	0.000
1	0.017
2	0.035
3	0.052
4	0.070
5	0.087
6	0.105
7	0.123
8	0.141
9	0.158
10	0.176
11	0.194
12	0.213
13	0.231
14	0.249
15	0.268
16	0.287
17	0.306
18	0.325
19	0.344
20	0.364
21	0.384
22	0.404
23	0.424
24	0.445
25	0.466
26	0.488
27	0.510
28	0.532
29	0.554
30	0.577
31	0.601
32	0.625
33	0.649
34	0.675
35	0.700
36	0.727
37	0.754
38	0.781
39	0.810
40	0.839
41	0.869
42	0.900
43	0.933
44	0.966
45	1

Angle (in degrees)	Tangent
45	1
46	1.036
47	1.072
48	1.111
49	1.150
50	1.192
51	1.235
52	1.280
53	1.327
54	1.376
55	1.428
56	1.483
57	1.540
58	1.600
59	1.664
60	1.732
61	1.804
62	1.881
63	1.963
64	2.050
65	2.145
66	2.246
67	2.356
68	2.475
69	2.605
70	2.747
71	2.904
72	3.078
73	3.277
74	3.487
75	3.732
76	4.011
77	4.331
78	4.705
79	5.145
80	5.671
81	6.314
82	7.115
83	8.144
84	9.154
85	11.430
86	14.301
87	19.081
88	28.636
89	57.290
90	

The tables on the left and right show the relationship between the size of an angle and its tangent. You can also use a scientific calculator to find the tangent of an angle. Since calculators differ, you may want to investigate how to use the tangent key on your calculator. You can use the tables on this page to verify your work.

You can also use a scientific calculator to find angle measures if you know the tangent ratio.

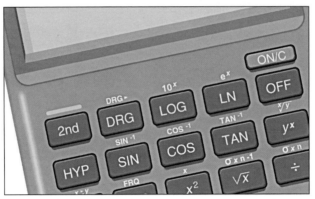

Use either the tables or the tangent key on your scientific calculator to answer the following problems:

21. What do you know about a glider with a glide angle of 4°? a glide angle of 35°?

22. Explain why tan 45° = 1.

23. Which angle has a tangent of 2? of 3? of 4?

24. How much does the measure of the angle change when the tangent value changes:

   a. from 0 to 1?

   b. from 1 to 2?

   c. from 2 to 3?

   d. from 3 to 4?

   e. from 4 to 5?

Solve each of the following problems using tangent ratios:

25. Suppose the glider on the right has a glide ratio of 1:40. It is flying over a village at an altitude of 230 meters, and it is 9 kilometers from an airstrip. Can it reach the airstrip? Explain.

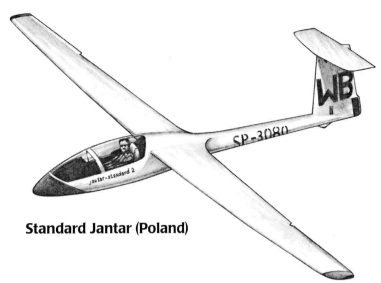

Standard Jantar (Poland)

26. One glider has a glide ratio of 1:40, while another has a glide angle of 3°. Which glider flies farther? Explain why.

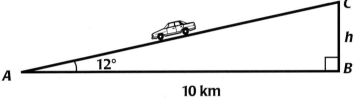

27. Compute the height of the road at point *C* for the drawing on the right.

28. At a distance of 160 meters from a tower, you look up at an angle of 23° and see the top of the tower. What is the height of the tower?

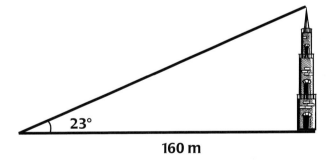

29. An electricity line pole makes an angle of 75° with the road surface, as shown on the right. How much does the road rise over a horizontal distance of 100 meters?

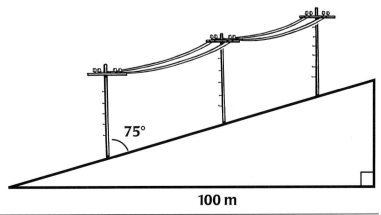

Summary

The steepness of a ladder, the angle of the sun's rays, and the flight path of a hang glider can all be modeled by a triangle such as the one shown below.

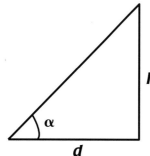

Steepness can be measured as the angle α or as the ratio h:d.

The ratio h:d is also called the tangent of angle α, or $\tan \alpha = \frac{h}{d}$.

Summary Questions

30. On a calm day, a glider pilot wants to make a flight that covers 120 kilometers. The glider has a glide ratio of 1:40. From what height must the glider be launched?

31. A glider with a glide ratio of 1:28 is launched after being pulled by an airplane to 1,200 meters above Lake Havasu City in Arizona. Indicate on the map on **Student Activity Sheet 18** how far the glider can fly if there is no wind.

Source: © 1997, Encyclopædia Britannica, Inc.

Section A. Now You See It, Now You Don't

Shown below are two boat models made with 1-centimeter blocks. Imagine that the boats are sailing in the direction shown by the arrows.

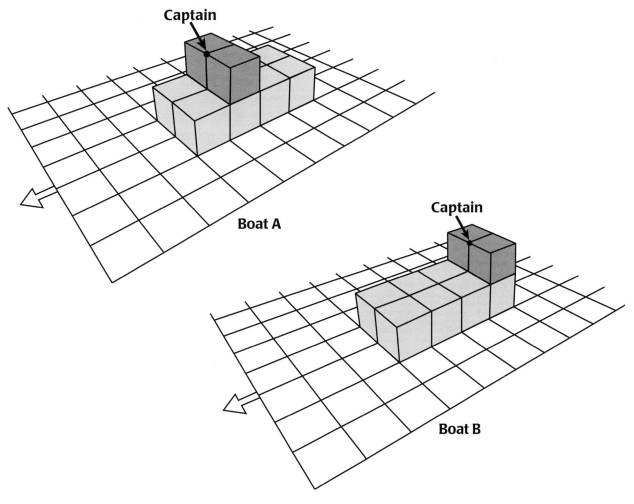

Captain

Boat A

Captain

Boat B

1. On graph paper or **Student Activity Sheet 7,** make side-view and top-view drawings of each boat.

2. On your drawings, include vision lines for the captain, who can look straight ahead and sideways, and shade the blind area.

3. How many square units is the blind area of boat A? boat B?

4. On your side-view drawings of each boat, measure and label the angle between the water and the vision line.

5. On which boat is the captain's view the best? Explain.

Section B. Shadows and Blind Spots

The height of a pyramid can be determined by studying the shadows caused by the sun.

Suppose that you put a stick into the ground near a pyramid. As shown below, the length of the stick above ground is 1 meter, and its shadow caused by the sun is 1.5 meters long.

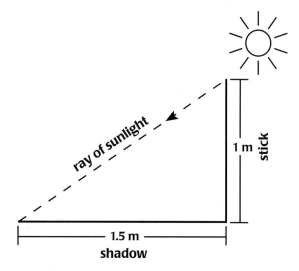

1. **a.** If the shadow of the pyramid is pointing northeast, which direction is the shadow of the stick pointing?

   b. From which direction is the sun shining?

The picture below shows the pyramid and its shadow at the same time of day. The length of the pyramid's shadow, measured from the center of the pyramid, is 240 meters.

2. Compare the height of the stick and the length of its shadow to find the height of the pyramid. Explain your reasoning.

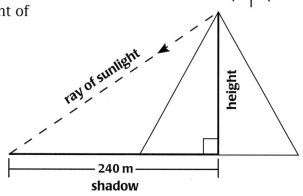

Section C. Shadows and Angles

1. Use a compass card or a protractor and a ruler to make side-view drawings to scale of the following ladders. Each ladder is leaning against a wall.

Ladder A

- The distance between the foot of the ladder and the wall is 3 meters.
- The angle between the ladder and the ground is 60°.

Ladder B

- The distance between the foot of the ladder and the wall is 4 meters.
- The ladder touches the wall at a height of 6 meters.

2. Determine the height-to-distance ratio for each ladder.

3. What is the angle between ladder B and the ground?

4. Which ladder is steeper, ladder A or ladder B? Explain.

Section D. Glide Angles

Use your calculator and the tables on page 44 to solve the following problems:

1. **a.** If $\tan A = \frac{1}{20}$, what is the measure of angle A?

    b. If $\tan B = 20$, what is the measure of angle B?

2. Marco is comparing two hang gliders. He takes one test flight with each glider from a cliff that is 50 meters high. The following picture shows the path for each flight. (*Note:* The picture is not drawn to scale.)

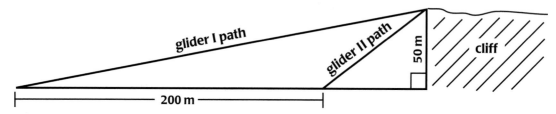

The glide ratio of glider I is 1:20, and glider I travels 200 meters farther than glider II. What is the glide ratio of glider II?

3. In the picture on the right, the measure of angle D is 45° and the measure of angle A is 30°. If the length of side BD is 10 centimeters, how long is side AB?

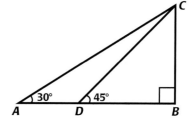

4. The following picture shows two cliffs that are 100 meters apart. One cliff is 20 meters high and the other is 30 meters high. Imagine that one hang glider takes off from the top of each cliff. The two hang gliders have the same glide ratio and land at the same location. How far from each cliff do the gliders land?

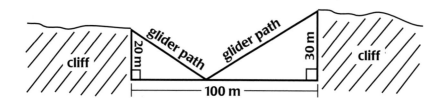

5. Suppose that a glider has a glide ratio of 5%.

    a. What you think a glide ratio of 5% means?

    b. What is the glide angle for this glider?

Cover

Design by Ralph Paquet/Encyclopædia Britannica Educational Corporation.

Collage by Koorosh Jamalpur/KJ Graphics.

Title Page

Phil Geib/Encyclopædia Britannica Educational Corporation.

Illustrations

2 (top) Phil Geib/Encyclopædia Britannica Educational Corporation; **2 (bottom right)** Paul Tucker/ Encyclopædia Britannica Educational Corporation; **3** Phil Geib/Encyclopædia Britannica Educational Corporation; **4** Phil Geib and Paul Tucker/Encyclopædia Britannica Educational Corporation; **6 (top)** Paul Tucker/Encyclopædia Britannica Educational Corporation; **6 (bottom), 8, 11–14, 15 (bottom)** Phil Geib/Encyclopædia Britannica Educational Corporation; **15 (top)** Paul Tucker/Encyclopædia Britannica Educational Corporation; **16–18, 22–24, 26–31, 34–35, 37** Phil Geib/Encyclopædia Britannica Educational Corporation; **38** Paul Tucker/Encyclopædia Britannica Educational Corporation; **39–44** Phil Geib/Encyclopædia Britannica Educational Corporation; **45** Paul Tucker/ Encyclopædia Britannica Educational Corporation.

Photographs

1–2, 7 © Els Feijs; **9 (top)** © Alastair Black/Tony Stone Images; **9 (bottom)** © Milton & Joan Mann— CAMERAMANN INTERNATIONAL, Ltd.; **10, 15** © Els Feijs; **22** © Jan de Lange; **29** © Els Feijs; **38** © Stock Montage, Inc.; **48** © Guido Alberto Rossi/The Image Bank.

CURC
Math
Second
MIC
Gr.7
v.8
1998

DATE DUE

GAYLORD			PRINTED IN U.S.A.